Sylvia Chioma

Cut off

A true-life FGM story

Accept the 'cut' or be childless? Against her wishes,
Aduke must choose between the two.

A GIRDLE'S INITIATIVE

Quadrant Books

First published in 2021 by Quadrant Books
A member of the Memoirs Group
Suite 2, Top Floor, 7 Dyer Street, Cirencester, Gloucestershire, GL7 2PF

CUT OFF

Paperback ISBN 978-1-86151-319-9

Typeset by RL Design, Cirencester
Printed and bound in Great Britain

CHAPTER ONE

In The Belly Of A forest

It was sunset. The sun was about to drop behind the long rows of tall pines and towering mahogany trees that stood like terrifying bouncers ready to fend off trespassers from the forest. The silver lining covering the clouds overhead was steadily transforming into a black blanket creeping over the forest.

A soft breeze slithered from the horizon and rustled the branches of the trees. It glided past the branches and stroked the birds' feathers, making them flap their wings, twitter and shift their perches in quick succession. The forest was enchantingly quiet with only a whisper of the wind, but suddenly the silence was broken by a high-pitched, squeaky female voice.

"You will NEVER, I repeat, NEVER carry a baby in your womb! You will NEVER hear the cry and laughter of a baby in your home! You will NEVER breastfeed a baby till you die! You will NEVER find peace in your home!"

For whatever reason, the strange haggard-looking old woman just went on showering torrents of curses on me without remorse. She wore a faded Ankara blouse and wrapper without any footwear to protect her feet.

I was in a strange place, very far from my home in Lagos State. I didn't know how I had got there or met the old woman, but here I was kneeling before her like a slave, while tears streamed down my face. My hair stood on end as my body contracted. I trembled and sweated profusely as I puzzled over my dilemma.

I recalled the last time and place when I had been conscious of myself. It was in an eatery in Ikeja which I often used as a rendezvous to entertain clients. But that afternoon, I had gone there for privacy to bemoan my troubled life. I assumed my captors had trailed me to the eatery and spiked my drink somehow, and when I had passed out, they had kidnapped me and brought me to this old woman – maybe for ritual purposes or other sinister reasons. As a lawyer, I knew our profession had its own hazards – intimidation, abduction or assassination from aggrieved plaintiffs or appellants.

I knew we were very deep in a forest which I imagined to be the hideout of kidnappers and ritual killers. We were surrounded by shrubs and big, tall trees. Apart from the woman there was no one else in sight, though I periodically heard a terrible sound; the faint cries of people crying in pain and pleading for their lives, coupled with the metallic sound of cutlasses being honed.

I knew my life was in grave danger but somehow, I found my composure and spoke to the woman in a shaky voice. "Please mama, I am very sorry, how did I offend you?" I asked. "What did I do to you to draw these heavy curses upon myself? Tell me so I may ask for your forgiveness! I am really sorry for anything I have done to offend you. Please forgive me. Please, see me as your daughter and have pity on me!"

The woman had a wrinkled face and her head was clean-shaven. She groaned and dilated her discoloured eyelashes and looked at me with scorn. Treacherously, she bent towards me as if she wanted to pick me up but instead, she slapped me very hard on my cheek. I was shocked by the force. It jolted me and sent me sprawling backwards to the ground. The effect of the slap was unexpected – it was not like a feeble slap from an old woman. I thought I had gone deaf as I rubbed my cheek with my palm to soothe the pain.

She did not show a jot of pity as I groaned in pain and then staggered to my feet. Instead, she vented more vituperation at me like a viper.

"See you as whose daughter? I am not a wretched woman, so I could not have a wretched daughter like you. You wretched woman!"

That was rather a falsehood because my late mother looked better fed than her and besides, as a successful lawyer, I knew I looked better nourished than any of her daughters could do – that is if she had any. But this wasn't a time for such comparison as I was at her mercy. I needed to be humble if I really valued my life.

I was grief-stricken, and tearfully rubbed both hands to make my plea to her. but she shunned me and lashed out again.

"Shut up there! So, you want to know what you did, eh? You stubborn woman. So, you don't know you have offended the gods of the land? For that, you will be disgraced as a barren woman till you die! And let me tell you this – no one can break those curses on you, NOBODY! There can be no deliverance for you!"

After striking me, she squeezed her face while contracting her nose and mouth to draw out phlegm from her nostril, then spat it out at my face. It was disgusting, but I bore the humiliation. Then she shoved me aside and made to leave the scene, but as she turned and walked away with brisk steps, I decided this time around that I would not plead with her, not after she had hauled curses on me and wanted to leave without explaining who she was, how I got to the forest and the reason why she had cursed me. Instead I would confront her. Desperate times need desperate measures, and this was one of them.

I mastered my pain and dashed after her, flinging myself onto her with all the strength I could muster. I was bent on using my strength to force her to answer my questions and break the curses on me – after all, she was just an old woman and I could overpower her very easily, so I thought. Besides, none of my captors were around to save her.

She lost her balance as I flung myself on her and fell onto the ground. I mounted her, gripped the collar of her blouse and threatened her in a furious voice.

"Mama, I don't know who you are, let alone offend you and your gods as you have claimed! I don't even know what I had done to you to draw your curses. If you don't break them, then before I die I will kill you first!"

She reeled in pain from the fall and stared into my eyes with scorn. Then, without saying a word, she started laughing hysterically at me.

Did she think it was an empty threat or what? I became

furious and burst out, "Mama, I am only respecting your age! If you don't tell me who these gods are and how I have offended them, you will go and join them very soon. I won't even pity your family members! I want to know who you are, and why you have cursed me. I know I have done nothing wrong to you or any of your children. Does this have anything to do with a case I won in court against you or any of your family members? Mama, speak out or I will kill you here!"

I was really bent on my words, but she wasn't scared a bit and just kept on laughing frantically.

Then the unbelievable happened. As I stared in surprise at her, her body suddenly became lifeless. I became alarmed. I climbed off her and placed my hand on her heart to feel her pulse. There was no sound – she was surely dead. I whimpered, thinking I had killed her, but suddenly she shoved me violently and sent me reeling to the ground on my back. Swiftly, she mounted me and started hitting me all over my body. I couldn't understand the source of her strength – was she on drugs or what?

I tried to fight back but she was just too strong for me. She subdued me and spat at me countless times while hitting me. Then she pulled something out from her wrapper. It was a knife – a red kitchen knife. She brandished it at me and made to stab me with it.

I was so alarmed that that I threw her off me with all the strength I could muster. I quickly pulled myself up and fled, then raced away without even taking a look back to say if she was chasing me or not. I wasn't going to wait to be killed and then buried in an unknown place. I thought about Kunle, my husband, and wondered if he'd have an inkling I had been kidnapped and whisked into this forest.

The thought of him and the desire to see him again gave me more strength, and I intensified my run. It was like hell running through the shrubs and thorny bushes. The spikes cut deep into my skin and drew blood from it, but I bore the pain and didn't care about the wound. I needed to run to safety to see my husband and family again – that was all I cared about.

After a short while I stopped in my tracks, convinced that I must now be far from the woman. I rested both hands on a tree and panted as I tried to catch some breath. Then, I looked back to see if she was on my trail and my heart skipped a beat. She was running fast towards me, wielding the knife.

I started off again and ran deep into the forest, screaming for help, but nobody was in sight. Unfortunately, I then tripped over a big stone and fell to the ground. I cried out in pain. I picked myself up and rubbed my big toe to relieve the pain. I was drained and limping.

Finally I collapsed to the ground. I tried to lift myself but couldn't – it was like I was glued to the ground. I tried to jerk myself up, but a mysterious force just pinned me to the ground. This forest was certainly a bedevilled place.

Tears streamed down my face as I started shouting for help. I knew I would be dead if this woman caught up with me. I groaned in pain and in my predicament, I looked around to see if she was still after me. I was relieved to see that she was no longer in sight, and thought perhaps she had stopped chasing me and turned back. I resolved to keep quiet and sneak out of the forest when the light began to fade.

I just don't know how, but suddenly she appeared in front of me. I had not heard her footsteps or the cracking sound of bushes; she just stood in front of me, a menacing figure. This was a terrible mystery.

I tried to gather the strength to pick myself up to flee, but she pounced on me, pinned me down, slapped me a couple of times and started tearing my dress to shreds. Soon I was completely naked. For the umpteenth time, I tried to ward her off, but I could not. My hands would not work properly. I tried to shout for help but I could not – I had lost my voice. It was as if she had cast a spell on me, because all I could so was to lie subdued and sprawled like a fallen statue on the ground.

She placed her bony hand on my belly and made to cut open my womb to perform whatever evil act she was bent to do on me. But then, for no apparent reason, she dropped the knife, clenched her right hand and began repeatedly using her fist to hit my stomach very hard to break what was left of my feeble resistance. She ignored my tears and plea. Instead, she spread my legs wide and picked up the knife. Then she began using it to roughly shave my pubic hair.

I was in severe pain because the knife was very blunt and it was forcefully scraping the hairs from my pubes as if a handful of hair had been grabbed and pulled from my head.

How can anyone be this brutal? I wondered how many people she must have killed in that forest. Judging by the way she had so mysteriously overpowered me and scraped off my pubic hair, I began to think she was the priestess of kidnappers or ritual killers. I had heard many stories of escapees from ritual dens who disclosed that the ritual killers first shave the head and the pubic hair of their victims before killing them for their diabolical sacrifices.

I was shattered. Now I knew I was face to face with

certain death, never to see my husband again. "Oh Kunle, I will never see you again!" I moaned.

My would-be-killer was busy shaving me. Then joyfully she suddenly burst into a self-composed song.

"The road is now clear for me to do what I want with you... the road is now clear, oh oh oh... This is what the gods of the land need from you... this is what the gods of the land need from you, oh oh oh... I just need to CUT it off from you and offer it to them... I just need to cut it off, oh oh oh..."

She went on singing in her guttural voice. Then she placed the knife on the top part of my clitoris and cut off a great chunk of it. I didn't see the blood, but I knew I was bleeding profusely, as I could feel warm liquid gushing down my legs. The pain I felt could not be described in words. I twisted in pain beneath her and started crying.

"Mama please, God knows I had done nothing to you. Mamaaaa, please!"

CHAPTER TWO

The Edgy Bus Ride

Ponmile, ponmile
Baby ponmile
Ma lo ni oko meji
Tori ope ti o sun le
Ponmile, ponmile
Oyaa baby ponmile
Ma lo ni oko meji
Tori ope ti o sun le
Ma lo ba wan di adelebo e
Wa gba certification ye
Won n be ni abule
Be ni Lagos ye...

The song 'Ponmile,' the music of Reminisce, boomed discordantly from the ripped twin loudspeakers in the famed Lagos State yellow and black-striped commercial bus. Yet it sounded harmonious to the ears of the dark-complexioned driver as he sang along, jumbling up the lyrics.

He was middle-aged and clad only in a singlet and Ankara trousers. He was in ecstasy as he hummed the song and swung his head side-to-side to its rhythm, and deftly veered the bus from the main road into the untarred streets to beat the traffic jam. He manoeuvred the bus from street to street and heaved a sigh of relief as he came out farther up the main road where the traffic was less.

"Ponmile or kpomo, or what is he jumbling over there? Driver, that music is too loud! Please, turn down the volume," One of the passengers suddenly burst out. He couldn't contain his anger any more and stammered. "Or... or do you want to burst our eardrums with those damaged speakers? If you can't repair them or buy a new set of speakers, stop playing music in your bus. You cannot force your passengers to be entertained!"

The driver groaned, frowned and momentarily took his eyes off the road to peek at the rear-view mirror to size up the passenger before answering. He replied abusively, "Turn wetin down? Na, your papa buy me bus wey you wan begin to dey control me inside, Oponu [stupid person]? Go and buy your own motor!"

Instantly, the other passengers, who all along had been quietly putting up with the noise of the speakers, lashed out at him en masse.

"You called him 'Oponu'?" shouted one. "If he and the other passengers didn't board your bus, how would you make money to feed yourself and your family? You transport drivers are too arrogant and foul-mouthed! All of una kuku be agbero! Useless man!"

"Look at this driver!" said another. "Shey na club or party we dey? Abeg turn down that thing make we hear word, yeye man! See as his forehead big like satellite dish?"

"Hey driver, you better keep your mouth shut and turn down that mess you call music so I can receive an incoming call," said a third passenger. "What sort of crazy bus did I get on?"

Another said, "Stupid driver, we are paying for this ride. We have the right to tell you what we want and you have to obey them with your mouth kept shut! I don't blame you – it's the person that hired out this bus to you, because I know you cannot afford to buy a tyre, let alone the bus. See how hungry he looks!"

Not wanting to be bullied, the driver swiftly engaged

them, one after another, in the tirade of insults but the verbal firepower of the passengers was superior, so, he piped down, turned off the stereo and swore under his breath. He drove on quietly but now roughly, which then drew the rage of other drivers as they ranted at him and dragged along the road with him.

"Abeg driver, take it easy. See trailer by your side. Driver, please!" another alarmed passenger pleaded with him in Pidgin English.

"What the hell is this man driving?" another passenger shouted. "Do you want to condemn us? Can't you see that the shock-absorbers on your bus are very bad? It's like the ogogoro [local gin] you drank this morning has started disturbing you! Let me get out if you want to go on with this crazy driving."

"Just look at how he sped past those police officers, but all they could do was to stare at him! Are they not supposed to have gotten suspicious and flagged him down for his reckless driving? This is how criminals drive past them while they look the other side. Naija Police sha!" Another one exclaimed.

There was another round of uproar before he reduced his speed.

Afterwards, when normality had been restored, one male passenger turned to the female sitting beside him and started a conversation. "I like that 'Ponmile' song by Reminisce – it preaches tolerance in a marriage," he said. These days, there are many bleeding homes and broken marriages. I mean, you get to see the married ones cheating on their partners and searching for love in the wrong places."

She nodded approvingly and replied, "That's true. Ehen, that even reminds me – how about that Ronke Shonde's case? I hope they haven't swept it under the rug like other gender-based violence cases that cost the lives of the wives."

"It's still in court but really, it's like she cheated on her husband," another male passenger, who was dressed in a suit, replied. "Didn't you read in the newspapers that her former boss disclosed to the police that she and her alleged lover were former colleagues and left his company after a month?" He turned to the lady and resumed, "I'm not trying to accuse or condemn her but if nothing really was going on, why did they leave that company, almost at the same time, and why did they later link up in Abuja? I'm sad she died and I'm sorry to say this, but it's like she was cheating on her husband."

"Ehen, even if she was cheating Nko – was that why Lekan beat her to death? Oga see, can Lekan swear on his life that he did not cheat on Ronke, not once but on several times?" The female passenger fired back and went on as she stammered in an emotional voice, "Even... Even if he had evidence, why didn't he approach his in-laws or confront her lover rather than kill her? God will punish that man wherever he is today. Yeye man!"

Another female passenger expressed her disapproval. "Cheating or not, no man has the right to hit or beat any woman, let alone take her life. Though women cheat just as much as men do, men cover their tracks better. Men actually cheat more!"

Another young female passenger carried on, "Abi o... Men are the worst culprits in this cheating game – they will chop and clean their mouths as if they didn't do anything. It is just that we, women, are easy to deceive. I doubt if there's a man who wouldn't cheat on his wife when given that chance. All men are the same!"

The conductor, who was alternating between listening to the conversation and 'shadowing' for passengers, tucked his head into the bus and cut in, "If men dey cheat or pursue women, no be women dem cause am? Na so-so short and tight dresses una dey wear. All una body go come show and point out yakata. No be food wey you give dog, dog go pursue chop?"

All the passengers burst into laughter.

"Please Lagosians, a point of correction here: it is

not all men that cheat on their women. There are some men who are different. Yes, men who are the real men." Another male passenger, who had earlier conducted a 'bus church service (evangelism)', challenged the other woman. He went on, "By the grace of God, I am a Pastor and since I married my wife I have never..."

A third female passenger, at the last seat, angrily retorted – from her look, it was obvious she was a trader as she reeked of the acrid scent of onions – and chided him. "Abeg, make we hear word joor. Na Pastors own worse pass sef! You have never done wetin? I dey follow you waka go everywhere? All of una na the same thing except the one wey no get that 'thing' between his two legs. No be one yeye Pastor for my area RAPE one small five-year-old girl with the pretence say he wan do deliverance on her. Men who are the real men koh; Men who are the real men nii. Shioor."

He was very peeved and raised his eyebrows, but before he could react, the bus went into uproar as everyone started talking at the tops of their voices and wanted to be heard at the same time. They were all trying to outdo each other on whose point was more convincing or authoritative. The bus was like a warzone – it was a battle of the sexes, a struggle for power between women and men.

I don't know how the conversation began, because I boarded the bus midway into the journey, but all the while they lambasted the driver and pondered on the Late Ronke Shonde's predicament while correlating with other couples they knew.

I didn't say anything because I had my own marital problem – a problem that had been tearing my home and life apart for a long time. This problem was bent on snuffing the life from me. Hard as I tried to extricate myself from it, it formed a ripple around me, getting big and bigger. It was a life-threatening problem – whether I should go for it or not?

I peeped through the window at nothing in particular and sank back into my thoughts, but was somewhat sharply taken aback by the sudden intrusion of one elderly bespectacled female passenger, who had been quiet all through the bus ride. She cleared her throat and chipped in with a cool tone.

"Your generation is plagued by infidelity and broken homes and marriages because you have allowed civilization to deceive you," she said. "Just because of civilization and wanting to adopt European customs, you have abandoned most of your core traditional practices that would have prepared the married ones among you for the challenges of marriage. There is too much rancour and distrust in marriages today. In our time, it wasn't this bad because we…"

The bus became quiet except for the distant noises randomly coming from outside. The passengers paid keen attention to 'mama' as she rattled on.

"See, most of our wives and daughters of today are promiscuous because your generation have abandoned the rite of passage of the female circumcision, or what Oyinbo people are deceiving you people by calling Female Genital Mutilation (FGM). Ask your parents this if I lied. In the olden days, it was compulsory for circumcision to be done for both male and female to protect them from certain things, especially in marriage. It is something we did, our forefathers used to do it and it was handed down to us. But you generation of today have abandoned it and of course, are suffering for it.

"You people don't even know that if the female is not circumcised, she will have a strong urge for sex. The sexual drive is located in the clitoris and that is why it is cut off. It is to curb promiscuity by reducing the libido.

"That is not all. This female circumcision is done to stop promiscuity. Also, when a woman wants to give birth, if she is not circumcised the baby's head may break – this is according to Yoruba tradition."

The passenger in the suit turned to mama and replied,

"Mama, with all due respect to you and our tradition, I must say those things are barbaric and senseless. You people practising FGM claim that the need to 'cut' these girls early is in order to stop promiscuity later in life, but the fact is that, for some women, the clitoris, among other areas like the nipples and inner thighs, can make them aroused, so do you cut off their nipples or their thighs because it can make them aroused? Mama see, promiscuity is a thing of the mind – it is a CHOICE! Besides, do you know that in May 2015, former President Goodluck Jonathan signed a Federal Law banning FGM?"

She raised her tone and fired back, "Ban koh, ban ni! How can the Government ban a tradition that has been inherent from generation to generation? Let me tell you this: female circumcision is done to our daughters for the fear of infertility. Any woman who is not circumcised cannot give birth, so it is done to prevent infertility. The reason many wives or women have failed to give birth is that female circumcision wasn't performed on them. No female circumcision, no baby! FGM is a rite of passage into fertility!"

That really jolted me, because mama had just confirmed something my mother-in-law had confronted me with about two weeks ago. My mind drifted back to our talk.

"Aduke, my daughter," she had said. "You've been married to my son for over six years now but no child to show for it yet. I know you both have been certified medically fit to have children but I've been thinking about the cause of your barrenness with a view to proffering a solution, and I believe I have one if you would just open up to us. So, my child, let me ask you this: do you know if you were circumcised as a baby? Because if you were not, this might be the reason for your barrenness."

Of course I wasn't 'circumcised' or 'cut' because my parents were among the highly educated anti-FGM people. They didn't permit any of that 'primitive stuff' on any of their three daughters and besides, as a lawyer, I knew the nitty-gritty of FGM – I knew that the World Health Organization (WHO) had branded it as 'a harmful practice on girls and women and a violation of human rights'. Also, I knew FGM has no health benefits but plenty of risks instead – as well as disfiguration and loss of sexual pleasure, it can lead to incontinence and other bladder issues, infection, psychological damage, disordered periods, sexual dysfunction and death (from excessive bleeding)!

Let me make it clear here: FGM is not the same as male circumcision. FGM is 'literal' mutilation while male circumcision isn't. If a boy had the head (glans penis) of his penis cut off, then it would be considered mutilation. The glans is anatomically homologous to the clitoral glans of the human female. Typically, the glans is completely or partially covered by the foreskin, except in men who have been circumcised.

So, why should I agree to this crazy culture-imposed cut? And there sat my mother-in-law, trying to persuade me to go for a deadly cut at my mature age! It's like she wants me dead so her son can marry another woman. I gave her a clear-cut answer that I wasn't 'circumcised' and that I wasn't superstitious enough to believe it had anything to do with my womb-lock! For simplicity, I told her that nobody and nothing in this world could drag me to whatever 'thatched huts' those 'cuts' are done in.

I wandered back into reality as I recalled my mother-in-law's last advisory words: "Aduke, I won't force you because your generation of women are very stubborn because of your

chocolate and milk brains. You see, if you were not circumcised when you were young, there is still hope for you because you can still do it now to open your womb. Don't worry about your husband, because I'll discuss it over with 'my son' because I know an old woman in my village who can perform it on you soft and safe. And please dear, our religion supports it! Yes – it is in the Bible and the Quran! It's not only a cultural thing to do!"

I was bewildered whether or not my being 'uncut' had anything to do with my barrenness, but instantly I was able to recall those six nightmares I had had about that old woman chasing me and the red kitchen knife she plunged between my legs to cut off a chunk of my clitoris and draw blood from it. Those nightmares were very real, because they were a replay of what was actually waiting for me in the physical.

I had been married for six years and some months but no child to show for it yet – I hadn't even 'taken in' once, let alone become pregnant. Technically, I'm a barren woman just like the old woman who had taunted me. My husband had visited many urologists while I had seen the best gynaecologists, and both had certified me medically fit to have children.

Logically, people would conclude that my case had to do with one 'witch' from my hometown or husband's. I could understand my mother-in-law's frustration at my childlessness. Kunle is an only child and there has been heavy pressure on him to have children to cover up his parents' seeming 'unfruitfulness'.

But what I don't understand about those strings of nightmares is why the old woman kept on appearing with a knife and cutting off a chunk of my 'private part' with it. I just don't understand it, or if those nightmares had any connection with my predicament. Had I offended the gods for not being circumcised and because of that, they had shut my womb?

I quivered as I questioned myself. I was begging for answers and thought of opening up to my mother-in-law about the nightmares. But I decided against telling her because, if I did, I knew that her answers to the question of whether or not there wa's any connection would be in the affirmative. I knew that she would start interpreting the dreams and telling me that six times the gods had sent an old woman to frighten me into going for the circumcision.

She was expressionless as she looked straight into my eyes, awaiting my answers. I forced a smile, thanked her for her concern and assured her that I would think about it and then call her very soon when I was done.

I politely told her I was late for work, then stood and left. All through the hours at work, I pondered on her counsel and deliberated on my answers – yes or no. My misfortune and the swing of thought were telling on me as I became depressed and couldn't concentrate at work. So I made up my mind to hear from my husband before taking any decision, though I was certain that he would never give his consent to that primitive act. I was very sure of that, because he knew about FGM and its fatal consequences.

I don't know if Kunle's mom had discussed the circumcision issue with him before or after discussing it with me, but I was in shock when he played dumb to my greeting the moment I got back from work and instead, told me blatantly to get ready for the circumcision as soon as possible!

Then, for close to a week, he kept on pestering me to agree with his mom and immediately go for the 'cut'. I stood my ground but shockingly, for the first time in our marriage, he shouted at me. That was just the beginning, because days later, he beat the hell out of me for my refusal to go for the cut. That wasn't all; he threatened to beat me more until I changed my mind and went for the cut.

"What a life!" I moaned and jolted back to realisation that when I realised I was still in the bus. The other passengers had stopped discussing the FGM issue. Mama had dozed off, while some passengers were discussing the 'State of the Nation' in low tones.

Soon after this, I folded my arms across the seat before me and rested my head on my arms. Then I started daydreaming about my once-happy marriage. Yes, my home used to be the cynosure of all eyes – my marriage was near perfect, or so I thought by then. People regarded us as 'the ideal couple'.

Even when it was obvious to people that I was having difficulty conceiving, they still respected my home and moulded their marriages like ours – this was because Kunle didn't see our childlessness as a problem. Even if he did, he didn't show his frustration to me or anyone else. Instead, he showered me with love as if he had no care to father a child. I was his everything, whether children came or not. But here I was on a bus, lamenting the sad turn of fortune in my home. Tears started trickling down my cheeks. I sat straight up and quickly brought out my handkerchief from my handbag and dried my eyes with it in case other passengers saw them and start wondering what had suddenly come over me.

Hard as I tried not let it happen, my mindset took a repulsive flashback to the battering I had suffered at the hands of Kunle just because I tried to make him agree with me that his mom's advice could boomerang on me. I tried to explain to him about the risk on my life of the FGM, but he turned a deaf ear to me.

I became downcast as I relived the battering that had left me with a red eye, a swollen face and bruises all over my body. A tear trickled down my face as I peeped through the window and tried to take my mind away from my problem.

Somehow, I was forced to recall how Kunle pounded me and almost killed me in the process. That incident revealed the other side of a man I thought I knew.

CHAPTER THREE

The Other Side Of A Man

I'm not a feminist or a female chauvinist, but I know that every woman is vulnerable to domestic violence at one time or another throughout her life. Though domestic violence affects all women, not all women experience the same rate of abuse because these abuses come in different styles.

As I said, my parents were 'highly educated' and firm Christians. I can't recall a time my dad raised his hands against my mum, even though they had their differences and would quarrel. I grew up believing that all men were like my father, men who tolerated their children and wives' excessiveness without hitting them. I guess I was naive to believe this until I was given an admission into the University of Lagos to study Law.

It was during my second year that this heartbreaking incident occurred; by then, Funmi, my late dear friend, was twenty years old. She was my course-mate and best friend. In fact she was more than a friend to me and more like a sister. Although we lodged in separate rooms, we spent more time together than with any of our room-mates. Our friendship was magnetic, because we forged an unbreakable bond the first day we set eyes on each other; we always shared our deepest secrets. I was taken aback one afternoon when she came crying into my room and confided in me that she was two months pregnant and wanted to abort it.

At first, I was shocked to find that all along she had been indulging in pre-marital sex because she was one of the committee members of the Campus Christian Fellowship. But I overlooked her 'first' sin and tried to change her mind from committing the 'second' sin – the abortion. Funmi didn't listen to me and insisted on the abortion – she initially wanted to keep the pregnancy but decided against it when Dele, our course mate and her lover, who she branded her fiancé, refused to accept responsibility for it.

She was in tears as she swore that Dele was the only man she had gone to bed with. She even went on to swear on her life that he was the one who had deflowered and impregnated her. She was crying like a baby as she placed her head on my chest and soaked my T-shirt with her tears.

I was heartbroken when she told me how Dele had beat her pitilessly and humiliated her before his friends by calling her a 'campus whore', just because she had pleaded with his friends to persuade him to accept the pregnancy. She lamented to me that Dele even swore in front of his friends that he had never slept with her, and that the pregnancy was the responsibility of some other guy she was seeing behind his back. After that, he slapped her and violently pushed her out of his room and threatened to 'fix her up' (kill her) if she came near him again.

I was really embittered at Dele for hitting and humiliating her in the presence of his friends. She didn't deserve to be treated like a thief or a whore. My heart skipped a beat when I examined Funmi's face and saw the deep bruises. I then joined in her tears. I cried with her and began to sadly recall how since our first year in school, she had ceaselessly professed her love for Dele. She flaunted her love affair with him before the whole campus community. I also recalled that in that same first year, Dele would have deferred or stopped his schooling if it had not been for the sacrificial intervention of Funmi.

Dele came from a very poor home. His parents could not sponsor his education and so he was always in debt of one kind or another in school. It got so bad that the school authorities advised Dele to defer his admission and return later when he had raised enough money to fund his education. Of course, he agreed. He packed his stuff and went to see Funmi to break the news of his reason for suddenly discontinuing his education.

She was disheartened, but offered to bail him out by sharing her pocket money with him so he could pay for his fees and other upkeep. She even advised him to get a job as an 'evening tutorial teacher' off-campus just to alleviate 'their' problem. There were numerous times Funmi had to go hungry for days and nights just because she was sharing her money to sustain Dele's existence in school.

Back to her problem. Funmi tearfully disclosed to me that at first, she hadn't want any sexual relationship with him, but when he threatened to walk out on her for another girl, it was then she allowed him. She further claimed it was only once he did it with her – it was however a big disaster for her because she got pregnant.

How could this guy be this callous? After all the self-sacrifices she had made for Dele, his "thank you" to her was to beat and humiliate her in the presence of his friends, and worst of all, threatening to kill her if she bothered him.

I was fuming as I reflected on Dele's injustice to my kind-hearted friend. I was heartbroken as I watched her crying out her heart like a baby. I was short of words and didn't know what to say to her, or how to console her. I was confused about which was my main concern, whether to persuade her to abandon the abortion or to keep on consoling her for the battering she had got from Dele.

I was still deliberating when she suddenly got up, wiped her tears with the back of her hand, blew her nose with a handkerchief, straightened her dress, and thanked me for being a true friend to her. Then she hugged me and bade me goodbye while promising to come back later in the evening to see me.

That was the last time I saw her; that was the last I heard from her. I waited all night but she failed to come; so, after lectures the next day, I went to her room in the afternoon to see and comfort her. I was shell-shocked when I met some students crying. I pulled one of her tearful roommates to a side of the room and asked after Funmi.

My heart stopped beating for a while and I almost fainted when she lamented to me that Funmi had died while one of our medical students, who had offered to help her, was aborting her pregnancy. She tearfully narrated to me how one of the 'tools' he had inserted into her to abort the pregnancy had ruptured her womb and she had bled to death before any help could come her way.

As for the medical student, he abandoned her and fled from the campus when he saw the extent of the damage he had done.

I was shocked beyond words and started crying over the death of my best friend and swore that in my lifetime, I would never allow any man to violate me. That was the first time I had first-hand knowledge of a man battering his very good and supportive partner – of course, I never knew I was wrong because every man has his other side.

All through my relationships in the school, I was very careful about the kind of guy I dated, or even had as a friend. I kept to this until I met and married Kunle, and he was a very charming and understanding partner until the day he hit me and nearly killed me just because I refused to risk my life for the 'cut'.

No matter how gentle a man appears or how nice he has been over the years, there is always an other side he might show one day – this is the basis of the many domestic and sexual violence cases springing up daily.

Of course, the media are full of cases of marital disputes and separations – celebrities or not – but if you take a close look into the causes of these problems, it has a lot to do with the 'other man' or the 'other woman' – a third person in the relationship. This was not the case with my late friend, however.

As a lawyer, I have found that an alleged or confirmed act of cheating tops the reasons for domestic violence in many relationships or in a marriage. Yes, so much sacrifice and tolerance go into keeping a relationship going, but when things begin to fall apart, sometimes one or both parties look to other people to satisfy their needs.

I once read an online platform where a man rationalised that, "For sure it is men who are more likely to be unfaithful. The Nigerian culture and mentality support men and their promiscuity. Men are guiltier than women when it comes to having affairs, especially if you take into consideration their constant bragging about their sexual escapades. Women tend to be more loyal sexually than men."

However a female marriage counsellor strangely thought otherwise, saying: "Some people may want to deny this; however, I personally believe that women cheat more. They are just better at hiding it. Men find it harder to detect when a woman cheats as she is more discreet about it. We are always one step ahead of them, especially when it comes to having our girlfriends on our side to back up our cover story. Women don't get caught in the act as much as men do. Women are craftier and sneakier when it comes to these things. If a woman does it right, the man won't even have a clue. We are experts at keeping secrets. Up until now I still don't know some things about my girlfriend and I know she will never tell me. I have learnt to live with that, just as I would learn to live with cheating. What I don't know won't kill me."

As for me, I would say both men and women cheat. Cheating is not a man or woman thing, it is just who gets caught in the end. Whether the reason for cheating is convincing – boredom or temptation – many couples have to battle with the reality of cheating and other home-wrecking factors.

Cheating or not, domestic violence can happen to anyone, yet the problem is often overlooked, excused or taken lightly. It starts from threats and verbal abuse and then escalates to violent acts. It occurs within all age ranges, ethnic backgrounds and economic levels.

While women are more commonly victimized, men are also abused – especially verbally and emotionally.

Some say when it happens the woman must have done something to deserve it. But to suggest that is really wrong – no one deserves to be abused. The way a person behaves never gives permission for her partner to abuse her.

For the safety and sanity of girlfriends, wives and women, noticing and acknowledging the signs of an abusive relationship are the primary steps to ending it – but what signs should they look out for?

There are many signs of an abusive relationship. The most telling sign is fear of a partner. If a woman feels she has to walk on eggshells around her partner, constantly watching what she says and does in order to avoid a blow-up, chances are the relationship is unhealthy and abusive. Other signs that you may be in an abusive relationship include a partner who belittles you or tries to control you, and feelings of self-loathing, helplessness, and desperation.

But Kunle never showed any of these signs before he showed me his other side and swiftly pounced on me. Prior to that date, even after more than six years of our marriage and despite being childless, he still treated me like the 'queen' for whom he had knelt and asked for her hand in marriage back then.

I was still in the bus and wasn't paying attention to other passengers or what they were discussing as I had gone very deep in thought to wander back to just a week ago that I had my own very first taste of domestic violence.

* * *

The tastefully furnished master bedroom which doubles as my husband's private study was quiet save for the 'Onise Iyanu' gospel song by Nathaniel Bassey that was humming softly from the detachable Sony CD player which was docked in our king-size mahogany bed.

It was a new break of dawn that came with angelic beauty, like the voices of angels. The melodious chatter of birds flying deliriously in the sky had started renting the are. Like the radiance of the angels, the glorious rays of the sun in the sky had started brightening the world, and just like the ambience of angels, a gentle breeze had started blowing calmly all over the room.

The elements were clad in their best attire that morning, but I sprawled dejectedly on the bed after a long, lonely sleepless night of sadness because Kunle had refused to neither eat the meal I prepared for him nor talk with me, even for a second. He refused to respond to my greetings. He even abandoned the bedroom to sleep in the sitting room for two consecutive nights.

Though awake, I lay spread-eagled on the bed, gazing absentmindedly at the ceiling with bloodshot eyes from sleeplessness. I roamed endlessly in thoughts about my troubled life and was so deep in thought that I didn't see it when Kunle came in, opened the wardrobe, picked out his clothes and left me alone to bemoan my crumbling life.

My mind wandered back to the song of Nathaniel Bassey, 'Onise Iyanu'. If God was really gracious in mercy, why had He abandoned me to sink in shame and sadness? Why was God looking the other side while my husband and his family members tormented me, and even wanted to risk my life in the name of female circumcision?

I wasn't seeing this as a blasphemy or blaming God for my predicament but at least, I was expecting Him to be the 'Onise Iyanu' and turn my life around. Yes, my life really needed a turnaround – a turning point.

My name is Aduke Coker. I am in my early 30s and a lawyer; despite the rigours of my profession, I am a faithful member of one of the largest Pentecostal churches in Nigeria. With such a burden on me as a childless woman, I am still a committed Christian and participate in every handy Christian programme, denominational or not. I have fasted days and nights. I visited various Pastors and Alfas (when persuaded by my Muslim friends), yet my problem persists. What haven't I done to make me be a mother like my equals?

I was really deep in thought and began ruminating for a solution. Suddenly, I was dazed momentarily by a heavy sound. My cheek burnt with pain. I was in pain and felt dazed, until I heard Kunle's raging voice as he spat out, "Aduke, so you think I'm playing with you, eh? Are you not ashamed that after six years of marriage, you can't even take in for once? I've tried to convince you to obey mama and go for that circumcision so you can break this reproach of barrenness on you, but you choose to be stubborn and foolish! You irritate me, and I will make life miserable for you since you've chosen to make mine miserable too!"

It then dawned on me that Kunle had actually slapped me. I rued my life and held my cheek as I burst into tears. With my tear-soaked eyes, I stared in pain at him, but he barked out, "You are a useless woman and a big shame to your family and to womanhood. I honestly don't know how I got stuck with such an awful woman like you. Do you know what? When I'm done with you, you will end your miserable life yourself - you lazy and good-for-nothing wife. Everything about you irritates me."

It was just because of this minor issue of FGM – so I thought – that he had slapped me very hard and even called me many disgraceful names, though this was the first time. But really, since I stamped my feet in protest against the FGM, he became easily irritated at every little issue, though they were mostly non-existent or had been caused by him.

"Kunle, but I've done nothing but love and support you,' I said. 'Please, forgive me if I have done any wrong thing to you. If it's because of the FGM, I will do it for you. But please, give me more time to gather enough courage for the cut. I'm scared and do not want my psyche to affect it."

I sobbed and tried to calm him down, as he was at boiling point. I thought I had made headway, but then he pounced on me and began to beat me to a pulp. As he battered me endlessly, I cried my eyes out and continued pleading with him to forgive me for an offence I hadn't committed. But he was not done yet. He yanked me by the hair and dragged my almost lifeless body from our bedroom to the stairs. My eyes were sore and swollen – in fact I was temporarily blinded. I bore the pain as I looked in shock and with blurred vision into the unpitying eyes of my assaulter – a man I called my husband, the love of my life, a man I was always ready to do anything for.

He puffed and wiped his forehead, which was drenched in sweat, and stood before me with clenched fists like a boxer, waiting for me to gather my breath so he could start hitting me all over again.

I trembled as if I was staring at an assassin; I could hardly believe it that this was the same man I had so much loved and left home for, and sworn to spend the rest of my lifetime with, till death do us part. How men can change!

I tried to plead again, but blood trickled into my mouth. I hadn't noticed that my nose was bleeding profusely. I writhed in pain and used the back of my hand to wipe the blood from my mouth. Then I mustered a little strength and knelt before him. I pleaded with him to have mercy and spare my life, for old time's sake. But it fell on deaf ears. He used his right leg to stamp on my tummy and violently kicked me down the stairs. My head hit the railings, once or twice, and blood spilled from a gash. I cried in pain all through my rough roller-coaster ride from the top of the staircase to the bottom. This was the height of a husband's cruelty to his wife – for whatever reason.

I blanked out as I hit the floor. When I recovered, I found myself in a hospital with plasters on some parts of my body.

Much later, Kunle visited me and was very remorseful. He softly held my hand and in an emotional voice, pleaded with me to forgive him, but I was unmoved and uninterested. I stared up at the ceiling all through the time he was talking, sermonizing his plea and swearing that such 'bestiality' from him would never be repeated.

Indeed, I was a lawyer and could easily have pressed charges against him and got him locked up, but just like every other naïve woman secretly suffering from domestic violence, I was ashamed of what the public would say and chose to remain silent about it.

I just do not understand this 'streamlined mentality' of society that women are the major reason for the domestic violence they encounter in their homes or relationship. When a man gets home drunk and batters his wife because of the effects of the alcohol, they would say it is the fault of the woman. When a man has a 'side chick' and starts making the home unbearable for his wife just because he wants her out of his life for his new babe, the society would say it is the fault of the wife. When a man has a bad day and gets home and pours his frustration out on his wife by insulting or battering her, people will again say it is the wife's fault. Why all these thoughts about women being the cause of domestic violence?

I took a sober reflection on the many wives who had lost their lives in their home from domestic violence just because they chose to be silent and get killed rather than speak out and run for their lives!

Some days later, I was discharged from the hospital, but I had made up my mind. Though I was still having occasional pain in my body, I called my mother-in-law on the phone and meekly disclosed to her that, for the sake of the peace of my home, I was ready for the circumcision that would make me pregnant.

She was very happy and rendered adulation with my name in our native language. She went on to assure me that the 'cut' would be 'painless, speedy and successful' and then, twice gave me the description of the place. She promised to meet me there on our scheduled date.

Kunle was very happy too when I told him. He smiled and promised to make it up to me for showing his 'other side'. I was indifferent and stared at him with a cold face. Of course, I had made up my mind to show him *my* other side too. My other side was to become a very passive wife to him.

On the day of the cut, he left early for work while I got ready and joined this very bus en route to the supposed 'clinic' for the cut. I didn't want to drive to our rendezvous because I wasn't in the right frame of mind for such a long drive to an unknown destination.

The domestic violence I had encountered and the

FGM I was cajoled to surrender to had so shattered me that I knew I couldn't deal with driving on the ever-busy Lagos road while intermittently asking for directions to the place.

I sauntered across the road to call a taxi. I waited for a while, but didn't see one before the scorching sun forced me to join the bus that was heading in my direction. And I must admit that it was by divine providence that I went by public transport, because of the FGM enlightenment I got on the bus.

It is rather surprising that many government functionaries, high-ranking professionals, celebrities and elite of the society (etc), just because of their status, shun taking public transport. The reality is that they should descend from their high pedestal and mix with the masses by using the mass transport system once in a while, and like me, they'd be surprised at the valuable pieces of news they'd gather to move this nation forward.

The bus ride was edgy, but during it I became more informed about marital disputes, FGM and other stuff.

CHAPTER FOUR

A Cut Too Deep

The driver drove into a garage at Ikorodu and parked his bus while we got down. I wanted to approach the bespectacled woman as she walked slowly past me – it seemed she had vast knowledge about female circumcision. I was very scared for my life and wanted her confirmation that a woman of my age can go for the 'cut' and importantly, the possibility of surviving the cut at such a mature age. I had done some online research and discovered that 24.8% of Nigerian women between the ages of 15 and 49 are victims of FGM. I wanted a first-hand confirmation from her and also, clarification if really my barrenness had anything to do with the fact that I wasn't circumcised, and if there was a possibility that I would become pregnant after the cut.

But somehow I jettisoned the idea of approaching her and instead, crossed to the other side of the road to call a taxi to my destination, which mama had told me was a ten-minute drive from the garage. I flagged down a taxi. He slowed down to park by the side of the road just beside a newspaper stand, and as I hurried to meet him, my eyes caught a bold caption on one of the newspapers displayed there. The headline read with a rider:

AMBODE'S WIFE CONDEMNS FEMALE GENITAL MUTILATION

…Says Nigeria Can End Scourge By 2030

I was alarmed and quickly pleaded with the driver to spare me a minute to buy the newspaper. He did, so I went to buy the newspaper and later on, got back into the taxi after we had settled on the fare. I sat impatiently in the back seat and quickly flipped to the pages that had caught my attention. I began to read with full concentration and patience. I picked up every word, digesting them one after the other.

Lagos – Mrs. Bolanle Ambode, the wife of the Lagos State Governor, on Tuesday urged parents and nongovernmental organisations (NGOs) to unite with governments at all levels to ensure the eradication of Female Genital Mutilation (FGM) in the country.

Mrs. Ambode, who spoke to the media at an event to commemorate this year's International Day of Zero Tolerance for Female Genital Mutilation in Lagos, expressed optimism that female genital mutilation could be stamped out of Africa by 2030.

While urging government to put in place the right statutes to end the dastardly act, she stressed that all individuals and stakeholders should work together to achieve that purpose.

She also said that although the practice was well entrenched in the continent, with some countries recording up to 90 per cent prevalence among girls and women.

But she was optimistic that the situation was not hopeless if the current advocacy was sustained or increased.

According to her, "The pace of penetration of awareness seems slow because the practice is an ancient one, deeply rooted in our various cultures, but that does not make our efforts fruitless.

"Though progress may be slow, we are going somewhere as rural women, mothers and young girls, are becoming aware of the severe health implications of the barbaric practice."

February 6 every year is set aside by the United Nations (UN), as the International Day of Zero Tolerance for Female Genital Mutilation across the world.

Wow! Even the first Lady of Lagos State knew that FGM was barbaric, based on her words that 'though progress may be slow, we are going somewhere as rural women, mothers and young girls, are becoming aware of the severe health implications of the barbaric practice'".

I purred to myself. Then I trembled and began sweating. I read the whole story for a second time. I closed the newspaper with shaky hands. I asked myself if this newspaper wasn't a God-sent sign to me – a warning for me not to go for the female circumcision, for if not, what else was it?

Mrs Ambode had urged 'government to put in place the right statutes to end the dastardly act,' and yet I was about to risk my life for it. I tried to take in the warning, which seemed aimed at me.

I was confused and breathed heavily as I began thinking fast about the next step to take. I was about to change my mind and ask the taxi to return to the garage when my mother-in-law called. I didn't want to take the call, but something just pushed me to. She was very excited as she told me she was already at the place waiting for me, and that all was set for the 'painless' cut.

I told her I was a stone's throw away and briskly ended the call. I kept the phone in my bag as the driver had noticed my uneasiness and quizzed me, "Madam, I hope there is no problem? See as you dey sweat even as AC dey blow inside my taxi? Well, na the next turning be the place wey you dey go."

"No problem, Oga driver. I'm fine. Okay – the next turn? Thank you." I replied.

At the next turn he swerved into a long, potholed-filled street. The ride was dusty and bumpy, but he finally pulled over and stopped at my destination. I paid and thanked him as I got out his taxi.

I had made up my mind in the taxi to inform my mother-in-law again that I did not want the cut, but would wait for God to wreak His miracles on me and bless me with a baby. I looked around the compound; it was built with thatched roof and brown clay blocks, which were neither cemented nor painted. It was an old house, but it displayed the beauty of a rural Nigerian house.

I walked towards the door and knocked. I was bent on not entering the room but asking my mother-in-law to come outside so that I could tell her of my decision and then swiftly return to my home. But as soon as the door was open, I couldn't bear to say anything, because of the person who had opened the door. It was Kunle.

How the hell had he got here without telling me? Men can be very secretive at times. He hadn't made any attempt to tell me he was coming or give me any hint he would be coming down here to meet me. I thought he had gone to work instead.

He smiled and apologized to me for not informing me that he would be coming here. He went on to explain that he wanted to surprise me with his presence and he wanted to make me feel relaxed and safe for the circumcision.

I forced a smile and thanked him as I entered the house, but really, I wasn't happy with him. No sensible woman suddenly forgives and forgets the sins of a man who beats her up and treats her like an animal. Love has no part to play in that decision. A woman's anger supersedes any kind of love; after all, there is an old saying that "Hell hath no fury like a woman scorned".

Shortly after this, his mother came out excitedly from an inner room while showering me with sweet names. She was accompanied by a much older woman whom she introduced as Mama Ako Ila. I was relieved to see that she didn't look like the other old woman, the one who had tormented me in my nightmare.

Mama Ako Ila was very fresh – it was obvious she was making lots of money from circumcising people. She had gone grey everywhere on her head; even her eyelashes. But she had a very charming personality and smile.

I knelt and greeted both of them as they smiled and Mama Ako Ila asked me to sit while she prepared her 'surgery room'. We sat down on a couch, but I sat far away from Kunle and his mum – even with Kunle's presence, my heart was beating fast from fear and I began thinking fast of a way to convince them that I wasn't mentally prepared for the circumcision.

Within a minute, Mama Ako Ila peeped from the curtain and asked Kunle's mom and me to come into the room. Kunle smiled and whispered to me to be courageous as he was right there waiting for me to support and comfort me.

As we got inside and sat, Kunle's mom gave a long introduction to Mama Ako Ila; she said she was a well-known priestess who was an expert in child delivery and at taking care of all bodily ailments. She was famous in Ikorodu and its environs for her roots and herbs (agbo), which she used to cure convulsion, asthma, stroke and other terminal sicknesses.

She also made ethnic facial marks and incisions on sick persons' bodies to cure them in the traditional way, but principally, she was legendary at circumcising male children and cutting female genitals too, of any age.

The introduction was boring to me as I studied the room instead. It was a typical replication of a native doctor's room in most Nollywood movies – a red-oil side for libation with kolanuts, bitter kola, cowries and other weird stuffs scattered around it, calabashes and gourds. Then, I shuddered when I saw her tools. There were rusty bloodstained razor blades, bloodstained napkins and assorted liquid concoctions in small bottles and then, I saw the KNIFE – it was the same that that old woman in my nightmare had used to cut me with. There was no difference at all. It was the same knife – a red kitchen knife!

I didn't need any oracle to interpret my nightmare. I knew my life was in danger and that I had to run away if I wanted to live on. Instantly, I got up to flee but, they defied their old age and sprang up and held me down while they struggled with me to lift up my gown to pull down my panties.

I just couldn't understand where these two old women got their powers from; I was like a toy to them as they easily stripped me. I had just one source of help – Kunle! I called out to him and pleaded with him to rescue me.

But I heard him echo from the parlour in an emotional voice that he wished he could but he couldn't and that instead, I should please find enough courage to bear the cut and that everything would be back to normal for us.

As help wasn't forthcoming, I was forced to open up to them concerning my nightmares and my interpretation that something bad might happen to me.

Mama Ako Ila laughed at me and made interpretations to me that the nightmares were in accordance – that it was a warning to me as my parents had offended the gods of the land by not circumcising me, and that it was sacrilegious for an uncircumcised woman to marry a circumcised man. She went on to assure me that all would be well after the cut, and that she would give me anaesthesia to make me sleep deeply while she performed the short painless operation that would take away the reproach of my life from me.

I listened, but my mind wondered at the predicament of the thousands of helpless innocent girls and women who must have screamed in pain (anaesthesia or not) under the razorblade and sharp knife of Mama Ako Ila.

She disrupted my thoughts when she started lecturing me on the need for the FGM, surprisingly in unblemished English: "Apart from making fertility possible, female circumcision is beneficial because it is a good tradition and a religious requirement. In our culture, it is a necessary rite of passage to womanhood, which you have not been privileged to enjoy. My dear, this circumcision will ensure cleanliness and better marriage prospects, prevent promiscuity and excessive clitoral growth, preserve virginity, enhance male sexuality, and facilitate childbirth by widening the birth canal.

"Besides, just like you at this mature age, some women in Nigeria and Mali undergo FGM during early adulthood when marrying into a community that practices FGM or just before or after the birth of a first child.

"So, my daughter, do not see us as your enemies – we are only trying to make your womanhood enjoyable and eventually turn you to a woman. Within the next ten minutes, we will be through with all these, but first, drink this local anaesthetic that I brewed for you. You will not feel any pain; just relax and take your eyes away from the knife while I cut off the useless things on your private part."

Did she just say FGM "prevents promiscuity and excessive clitoral growth… preserves virginity"?

That's a big lie because I was not promiscuous, and I'm still not. I had no sexual adventures in school and was a virgin when Kunle married me, and he never complained about the size of my clitoris or that he didn't enjoy sex with me.

So where did all these myths about FGM come from?

However, I was not ready to fight back, because I knew it would have been useless. I collected the bottle from her and drank the bitter oily concoction and five minutes later, I was feeling sleepy and my body became nerveless.

She gently hit my knee with a hammer and surprisingly, I felt no pain. Then she gently spread out my legs and crouched between them. I fought to stay awake and watched as she picked up the knife and started cutting what I presumed to be my labia or clitoris.

Suddenly it happened…

I saw her shake and shriek in local parlance, "Mo, gbe o (I'm in trouble)!"

I was alarmed too and started praying that God should spare my life and not make this a serious case. She quickly picked up a white towel and began dabbing the blood that was rushing between my legs – it's like she had mistakenly cut my 'clitoral vein'. My mother-in-law was alarmed too, as she got up from the stool and stood beside her and was asking her what she could do to help. From the look of Mama Ako Ila's face, I knew something had gone wrong, very wrong. She used towels, one after the other, but the blood kept gushing out – she had cut me too deep and dangerously and couldn't control the overflow of blood. I was losing blood at a high rate. Mama Ako Ile was frightened and quickly got up and called Kunle into the room. Suddenly, I felt sleepy and dozed off but faintly heard them deliberating whether or not to call the medics to come and rush me to the hospital with an ambulance.

I opened my eyes briefly to see Kunle talking nervously on the phone, possibly to the medics. He looked at me intermittently with a tearful face. He came close to me, raised my head and placed it on his lap while he started rocking me gently and praying for me. That was the last I saw before I passed out.

I don't know how long I was out for, but when I regained consciousness, I found myself full stretched out on a bed, with my legs spread out. I discreetly looked over the scene of the ward and noticed an elderly man, who appeared to be a doctor. He was neatly dressed in a white lab coat with a stethoscope hung round on his neck. He was flanked by a middle-aged nurse, who looked radiant in her white body-fitting uniform with a cap to match.

Kunle and my mother-in-law stood by them, staring in shock as they awaited the result of the test the doctor had conducted on me when I was in a coma.

Mama Ako Ila was nowhere to be seen.

I heard the doctor lambasting my husband and his mother for selfishly attempting to waste my life in the name of covering their shame (for my childlessness in their family) by opening up my womb through FGM. He went on to enlighten them how the practice of FGM was cruel and barbaric and importantly, the statistics of the many lives that had been lost to the process due to heavy bleeding, just like the one that happened to me.

They were remorseful as he went on to inform them that FGM had been criminalised in Nigeria, together with the disapproval of the medicalization of it.

"See Mr Kunle, the medicalization of FGM whereby some health workers carry out these female circumcisions in an assumed 'safer and hygienic atmosphere' is wrong as well," he said. "The medicalization of FGM/C is illegal and efforts are being made to stop this. Even the Nigerian Medical Association is against it."

"Apart from the medicalization, all men should join the cause to end FGM because they are the custodians of the culture. Instead, most men are in denial or silent to the menace of this practice that has too often gone under the name of "female circumcision". This makes it sound as innocuous as what is done to baby boys, but it's actually otherwise. Female Genital Mutilation (FGM) will never end until men also throw their weight behind efforts to eradicate the potentially deadly practice!"

Then wait for this... what he said gave them a big shock.

"Mr Kunle Coker, your wife is two months pregnant, but I'm certain that the loss of blood will result in a miscarriage – it's just medically impossible for her not to lose the pregnancy. I'm not the type of doctor who minces words with patients, so, I'll advise that you and your household should be ready to hold your hearts for the loss. I'm really sorry to break such a piece of shocking news to you but right now, we are more concerned with reviving your wife than anything else."

Kunle turned pale and opened his mouth in shock with his arms folded across his chest while his mom placed her two hands on her head and began to regretfully shout, "Ha, mo gbe, mo' gbe!" (I'm in trouble).

They thought I was still unconscious, or he would not have broken such news to them. It was a piece of bittersweet news – I was pregnant, but I was going to lose the baby.

"I was two months pregnant? I'm pregnant at last?" I smiled softly with my eyes closed and then, sorrowfully purred to myself, "If only I had known that, I wouldn't have foolishly yielded to their threats and risked my life in the name of getting pregnant from the cut. So, the FGM or female circumcision had nothing to do with fertility, after all. What a life! What a lesson for others!"

Though I was bothered about losing the pregnancy, I left my hope to God and then chided myself for not having been able to detect that I was two months pregnant. In actuality, I did recall noticing the signs, but maybe due to the pressures from Kunle and his mom, I overlooked them as mere symptoms of sickness instead.

Soon after this the doctor and the nurse left my ward while Kunle's mom went downstairs. Kunle stood beside me all the while.

I turned my head sideways to take a look at him. He was a very good and caring man. If not for my mysterious delay in having a child for him, I knew he wouldn't have had cause to humiliate and domestically abuse me. I knew he loved and cherished me and of course, I loved him too, still.

Before we met, I had a disgust for men and kept them at bay because of the two near-rape experiences I had had, but Kunle came into my world and showed me that there are many men who have angelic hearts. I gave a wry smile as I recalled those two experiences.

The first one happened when I went to visit Lola, my friend. I got to her home but met her older brother instead, who told me she had gone to their mother's shop but would be back in a jiffy. I had to wait for her in the company of her brother, not knowing he had four friends waiting in his room and had already schemed with them to gang-rape me after he had spiked my drink. I was a virgin and tomboy then, and later wondered about the sensuality they saw in me. He offered me the spiked drink and left the sitting room, but fortunately I sensed a conspiracy. Quickly, I stormed into the kitchen and emptied the drink. My fears were confirmed when I saw the traces of powder on the base of the tetra-pack.

I quietly returned to my seat while he anxiously came into the room from time to time to check if the drug had taken effect on my body, but when he saw it hadn't and that time wasn't on his side, he became frustrated and called in his friends to drag me into his room. I started screaming at the top of my voice. My scream was so loud that it was my saving grace, as it attracted the attention of the neighbours and gateman who stormed into the flat and rescued me.

The second time was in my university days. I was living off-campus and was in a serious relationship with a guy whose closest friend was in our school. He was more or less a mutual friend, though I saw and treated him as a brother, but surprisingly, he came into my room one day and attempted to rape me. But for the timely intervention of my roommates, who were within earshot, he would have had his way, as they knocked frantically on the door and window when they heard my cries and struggles.

Those two near-rape experiences affected my psyche about men, not until Kunle walked into my life and changed that mentality with the way he treated me with love and respect despite my sexuality. Right there and then, I forgave him. I felt for him and decided to put the past behind me, though I knew there was a crack in our love that could never be mended.

Yes, I had forgiven him, but the truth is that when a man, for whatever reason, decides to be abusive and raises his hand to his wife, such a man should NEVER expect the same level of love he was enjoying from his wife prior to the abuse. A woman can forgive, but she will never forget being treated badly.

Impulsively, Kunle glanced at me and our eyes met, but his guilt made him take away his gaze from mine. He stole another glance at me but turned away and dropped his head when he realized I was still looking straight at him.

I had seen enough to know he had been crying his heart out – he looked shattered and broken. His head was still bent as I softly called him, "Kunle…"

He quickly turned and forced a smile. I smiled back and tried to say something to him but couldn't. Instead I started gasping for air while my eyes began to roll back into my head like a convulsive patient's.

In my oblivion, I heard him tearfully shouting, "Doctor, Doctor, Doctor! Aduke please, Aduke please, don't die, pleases…Adukeeeeeeee!"

He pressed the emergency bell to call out the medics and in a jiffy, the doctor, accompanied by a nurse, rushed into the ward. The doctor came closer to me and placed his stethoscope on my chest before making a gesture to the nurse. She dashed out of the ward and momentarily returned with a blood pressure cuff, which she fitted on my upper arm to feel my pulse. Then, she squeezed the bulb, which inflated the cuff, and listened to my heartbeat through another stethoscope that was placed on her ears.

She stared at me in shock before turning to face the doctor to make a despairing gesture at him. He understood, and stepped in front of her. He bent over me and started to pump my heart with his two hands in a bid to revive me.

Kunle was as white as a ghost. He was literally trembling and shifting his gaze between the doctor and the nurse, and asked in an emotional voice, "Doctor... Doctor please, hope no problem? Please, please, erm... erm... Is there anything I can do to help?"

The doctor was too busy with his attempts to revive me to answer him. He was sweating and stopped pumping my heart when he realised I wasn't responding. He turned and pressed another emergency bell, just above the one Kunle had pressed. At once, two nurses stormed into the ward. One pushed in a wheel stretcher while the other carried a medical tray, which was filled with sorts of injection equipment.

The doctor gesticulated to them to lift me up to the stretcher; they did and gently placed me on it, then, wheeled me away to the theatre while Kunle ran after us. He caught up with us and gently placed his right hand on my cheek while he used his left hand to join them push me into the theatre.

When I felt Kunle's hand on me, I forced my eyes partially open and was able to hazily catch sight of him before my eyes involuntarily closed itself again.

He was in tears amid his heartbroken, disjointed plea

to me. "Aduke, hold on please, Aduke! I need you in my life, please! I'm sorry for the pain I've caused you and erm... erm... erm... for putting your life at risk just because I wanted a child. Please, I regret my actions and I... I... I... will never forgive myself for making you go through this suffering! Please Aduke, forgive me. Please, hold on to life, please!"

His voice became fainter by the second. I really had sympathy for him and wanted to console him that all would be well, soon. I tried to give him a comforting smile, but couldn't. I tried to touch him, but couldn't. I tried to say something to him, but couldn't. My body was stock-still. My lungs were on fire and I was struggling to breathe. I knew I was hanging onto life by a thread. I knew it was just a matter of seconds before...

My eyes were tightly closed, but tears formed and forced their way out and slowly rolled down my cheeks. I took a deep, painful breath and plunged into darkness, 'cut off' from Kunle and his mom, 'cut off' from the hospital and 'cut off' from the society and their terrible practice of female genital mutilation.

What you need to know about female genital mutilation (FGM) in Nigeria

Female Genital Mutilation (FGM) is the partial or total removal of the female external genitalia. External genitals include the clitoris, labia, mons pubis (the fatty tissue over the pubic bone), and the urethral and vaginal openings. It has existed for more than 2000 years and is performed on girls from birth up to just before marriage, and sometimes beyond. Newborns, children, adolescents and young adults are affected – most girls undergo FGM when they are between seven and 10 years old.

It is sometimes called "female circumcision" implying that it is similar to male circumcision, but this notion is wrong because the degree of the female's cut is much more extensive, often impairing a woman's sexual and reproductive functions. Though it is difficult to verify reports of women's sexual experiences, physical complications from FGM often impede sexual enjoyment.

Also, FGM destroys much or all of the vulva's nerve endings, delaying arousal or impairing orgasm. Lacerations, loss of skin elasticity or development of neuroma (a tumour or mass growing from a nerve) can lead to painful intercourse. Some women undergo FGM during early adulthood when marrying into a community that practises FGM or just before or after the birth of a first child (Nigeria and Mali).

The horrifying fact is that 27% of Nigerian women are victims of FGM and 20 million of them have undergone it – this represents 10% of the global total. In reality, FGM is a massive problem in Nigeria because one in four Nigerian women between the ages of 15 and 49 years has experienced it, making the country number three in the world, following Egypt and Ethiopia.

THE ORIGIN OF FGM IN NIGERIA

There is no known traceable origin of FGM in Nigeria. It has been sustained for different reasons, including the stated need to maintain virginity, protect against barrenness, as a rite of passage, to follow social norms and for economic value.

The practice continues simply because "it is tradition." As a circumciser from Osun state said in an interview, "I was born into this practice. I do not know the history, but I can say it is as old as the tradition of tribal marks on faces."

It is estimated that 20 million women and girls have undergone FGM in Nigeria. Out of the six largest ethnic groups, the Yoruba, Hausa, Fulani, Ibo, Ijaw and Kanuri, only the Fulani do not practise it. FGM takes place in both urban and rural communities – the practice is most common in the south-west (Yoruba-speaking) and south-east (Igbo-speaking) parts of Nigeria at 47.5% and 49% of women cut respectively.

Osun, Ebonyi and Ekiti have been identified as the leading states in the practice of FGM. In Osun, the practice has been banned since 2004, but it is still the state with the highest prevalence rate in the country with 67.6% of women and girls undergoing the cut. Yet, despite the high prevalence of FGM, Osun State has very high rates of teenage pregnancy.

In some Nigerian communities, FGM remains common as a mark of superiority. In these places, it is a matter of pride to undergo FGM and as such, they attach a stigma to people who have not been cut. Some other communities believe that a baby will not survive if its head touches the mother's clitoris, so they cut the clitoris before a woman gives birth.

Besides, many tribes in Nigeria believe that 'female circumcision' is a form of initiation into womanhood or to ensure social cohesion and family integration. They claim to carry out this practice to reduce female sexual desire as a means to maintain chastity and fidelity, and as a way of increasing male's sexual pleasure. They believe that FGM stops promiscuity, but for some women, the clitoris, among other areas like the nipples and inner thighs, can make them aroused – so, do they cut off their nipples or thighs because it can make them aroused?

Promiscuity is a thing of the mind – it is a CHOICE!

What is FGM called in our local languages?

In Yoruba, it is called 'di dabe fun omo'binrin'. In Igbo, it is called 'ibi nwanyi ugwu' while in Hausa, it's called 'kaciyan mata'.

At what age is FGM performed?

This varies in different tribes and communities: in some places, girls are circumcised on the 8th day or before age 5 while others perform it before they reach adolescence and some when they are between 30 and 40 years old.

Who performs FGM?

Different communities have people who perform it, but the common ones are:

1. Traditional circumcisers
2. Traditional birth attendants

3. Elderly people (male/female)
4. Herbalists or members of secret societies
5. And unfortunately, some health workers!

How exactly is it done?

The procedure is done using tools like knives or scissors made by local blacksmiths. Some use razors or other sharp objects. The girl or woman is held down by the circumciser (sometimes with assistance) and the act is done.

Sedatives and disinfectants are not usually used. In some places, traditional medicine like herbs or fluid from snail is applied to aid healing of wound.

The four types of FGM

- Type I (clitoridectomy): Excision (removal) of the clitoral hood with or without removal of part or the entire clitoris.

- Type II (sunna): Removal of the clitoris together with part or all of the labia minora.

- Type III (infibulation): Removal of part or all of the external genitalia (clitoris, labia minora, and labia majora) and stitching and/or narrowing of the vaginal opening leaving a small hole for urine and menstrual flow.

- Type IV (unclassified): All other operations on the female genitalia, including pricking, piercing, stretching, or incision of the clitoris and/or labia; cauterization by burning the clitoris and surrounding tissues; Incisions to the vaginal wall; scraping or cutting of the vagina and surrounding tissues; and Introduction of corrosive substances or herbs into the vagina.

Type I and Type II operations account for 85 percent of all FGM. Type I is more common in the south of the country, and the more extreme methods, like Type III, are common in the north.

Does any religion support FGM?

There are no religious justifications for FGM. Though Muslims do carry it out, Christians do as well. However, there is nothing in the Quran or Bible that allows the mutilation of women. The origin of FGM is linked to Pharaonic heritage and African tribal rituals, and pre-dates Christianity and Islam.

However, some adherents of these religions believe

the practice is compulsory for followers of the religion. Because of this flawed link to various religions, and specifically to Islam, religious leaders have an important role to play in dissociating FGM from religion.

For example, while FGM is practiced in Egypt, which is predominantly Muslim, it is not practiced in many other countries with predominantly Muslim populations, such as Saudi Arabia and Pakistan.

The association of FGM with Islam has been refuted by many Muslim scholars and theologians who say that FGM is not prescribed in the Quran and is contradictory to the teachings of Islam. Equally, the Bible does not mention or recommend 'female circumcision' – in fact, Christian authorities agree that the practice has no foundation in Christianity's religious texts, and Christian missionaries in Africa were at the forefront of efforts to stop it; they led the way in referring to it as "mutilation".

The Government's efforts to abolish FGM

In May 2015, Former President Goodluck Jonathan signed a Federal law banning FGM. Currently in Nigeria, there is the Violence Against Persons Prohibition Act (VAPP), the only Act that prescribes punishment for the offence of FGM. Section 6 (1-4) of the Act provides for a set of punishments for this offence. Some of these punishments include:

i. Anybody who performs or engages another to perform FGM on any person is liable to a term of imprisonment not exceeding 4 years or to a fine not exceeding N200,000 or both.

ii. Anybody who attempts, aids, abets, or incites another to carry out FGM is liable to a term not exceeding 2 years' imprisonment or to a fine not exceeding N100,000 or both.

Also, it must be disclosed that just eight states in Nigeria, currently have laws prohibiting FGM and these are Lagos, Osun, Ondo, Ekiti, Bayelsa, Edo, Cross-River and Rivers.

One major drawback of the VAPP Act is its applicability. Currently, it only applicable in the FCT and also in Anambra State. All the other states in Nigeria have not yet ratified or domesticated this Act.

Does FGM benefit anyone?

For all the 'alleged' benefits of FGM, as being routinely performed as an integral part of social conformity and in line with community identity, it must be clarified that

FGM has no health benefits but many risks and complications instead.

Risks and complications of FGM

The risks and complications of FGM are common and they can lead to death, especially in areas where antibiotics are not available. In such areas, it is estimated that one-third of the girls undergoing FGM will die.

Also, where medical facilities are ill-equipped, emergencies arising from the practice cannot be treated and thus a child who develops uncontrolled bleeding or infection after FGM may die within hours.

The immediate physical problems of FGM

a. Intense pain and/or haemorrhage that can lead to shock during and after the procedure. Haemorrhage can also lead to anaemia.
b. Damage to adjoining organs from the use of blunt instruments by unskilled operators.
c. Urine retention from swelling and/or blockage of the urethra.

Long-term complications

a. Painful or blocked menses.

b. Recurrent urinary tract infections.

c. Abscesses, dermoid cysts, and keloid scars (hardening of the scars).

d. Increased risk of maternal and child morbidity and mortality due to obstructed labour. Women who have undergone FGM are twice as likely to die during childbirth and are more likely to give birth to a stillborn child than other women. Obstructed labour can also cause brain damage to the infant and complications for the mother (including fistula formation, an abnormal opening between the vagina and the bladder or the vagina and the rectum, which can lead to incontinence).

e. Infertility.

f. Some researchers describe the psychological effects of FGM as ranging from anxiety to severe depression and psychosomatic illnesses.

g. Many children exhibit behavioural changes after FGM, but problems may not be evident until the child reaches adulthood.

h. FGM is likely to increase the risk of HIV infection – often, the same unsterilized instrument is used on several girls at a time, increasing the chance of spreading HIV or another communicable disease.

How does FGM affect pregnancy?

FGM does not usually cause problems for a woman during pregnancy, but women who have been cut face unique health risks during childbirth. These include:

a. Prolonged labour or excessive bleeding after childbirth.

b. Higher risk for episiotomy during childbirth. A doctor makes a cut in the perineum, the flesh between the vagina and anus. There is also a higher risk that this flesh will tear on its own during birth. These risks are especially high for women who have had type III FGM.

c. Higher risk for caesarean section (C-section). Doctors who are unfamiliar with scars left by FGM may suggest a C-section. However, it may not be necessary. Women with type III FGM may have their vagina safely re-opened (defibulated) during pregnancy or in labour and delivery, but health care providers may not have the experience or training to provide adequate health care for women who have been cut. However, if a pregnant woman has been cut, she should open up to her doctors to save her lives and the baby's.

Antenatally, women who have been cut should be assessed and, if necessary, offered deinfibulation before the birth because multidisciplinary care is needed for such women.

d. Risks to the infant include low birth weight (smaller than 5½ pounds at birth), breathing problems at birth, and stillbirth or early death.

Reasons for supporting FGM

Reasons for supporting FGM include the belief that it is a "good tradition", a religious requirement, or a necessary rite of passage to womanhood, that it ensures cleanliness or better marriage prospects, prevents promiscuity and excessive clitoral growth, preserves virginity, enhances male sexuality, and facilitates childbirth by widening the birth canal.

There is a direct correlation between a woman's attitude towards FGM and her place of residence, educational background and work status. Urban women are less likely than their rural counterparts to support FGM. Employed women are also less likely to support it. Women with little or no education are more likely to support the practice than those with a secondary or higher education.

Most women who have had the FGM procedure are strongly in favour of FGM for their daughters.

The medicalization of FGM

The World Health Organization (WHO) has an explicit policy that FGM/C, in any form, should not be performed by any health worker, yet in Nigeria and other countries, it is increasingly performed by health-care providers, which is very alarming.

The medicalisation of FGM is proposed by some health professionals to reduce the incidence of complications, but it will not reduce the long-term complications and thus, its performance violates the code of medical ethics.

It is unethical that the very people who are entrusted to care for people and bound by the professional health ethic to 'do no harm' are those carrying out FGM procedures now. In reality, medicalisation is not a solution for FGM; instead, it simply institutionalises it and reinforces the practice.

What is the medicalisation of FGM?

This includes, but is not limited to:

- Any FGM procedure carried out by a healthcare professional or in a healthcare facility (at home or abroad).
- the provision of medical equipment for the use of performing FGM.
- the carrying out of symbolic cutting as an alternative to FGM;
- providing medical training to traditional cutters and those carrying out FGM.
- any procedures to re-establish FGM after giving birth (reinfibulation).

The disadvantages of medicalisation

While some people have argued that medicalisation of FGM reduces the risk of infection and danger from complications such as blood loss, this argument ignores the fact that FGM is abuse. No form of FGM is ever acceptable and medicalisation neither makes the procedure safe nor addresses the long-term physical and psychological harm caused by FGM.

In addition, there have been some recorded deaths during procedures of medicalised FGM in some places.

Yet one of the biggest problems of medicalising FGM is that it hinders attempts to eliminate FGM around the world by giving medical backing to a procedure that is not only dangerous but ethically, morally and in most cases, legally wrong.

Today, more women are patronizing medical staff, though traditional practitioners are still active – typically, traditional practitioners perform FGM with sharp stones, broken glasses, scissors, or unsterilized razor blades without anaesthesia, but with medicalization, health professionals (doctors, nurses, and midwives) are increasingly performing FGM, though this trend might reduce the pain and/or the risk of infection – it will not prevent other complications.

In some contexts, health workers also carry out reinfibulation of women and girls after childbirth. Health workers are however well placed to play a strong role as advocates for change, not least because they are well aware of the complications and harm caused by FGM.

Ensuring the health system is brought into the discussion of ending FGM will be critical to its ending.

Can we do anything to prevent medicalised FGM?

Yes – it can be prevented when we stop taking our babies

or ourselves to these healthcare providers. Together we can end FGM.

Human rights efforts

FGM violates human rights conventions that protect women and children from cruelty and violence and ensure them "bodily integrity" and access to health care, education, and self-realization. Some of these conventions are:

- The Universal Declaration of Human Rights (1948).
- The United Nations Convention on the Rights of the Child (1959).
- The African Charter on Rights and Welfare of the Child (1990).
- The United Nations Convention on the Elimination of All Forms of Discrimination Against Women (1992).
- The United Nations Declaration on Violence Against Women (1993).
- The World Conference on Human Rights, Declaration and Programme of Action, Vienna (1993).
- The United Nations High Commission on Refugees, Statement Against Gender-Based Violence (1996).

FGM eradication has also been included in resolutions and action plans at various international conferences, including the 1995 International Conference on Population and Development and the 1995 Fourth World Conference on Women.

GIRDLE is a sensitization programme to combat antisocial practice, violence and sexual abuse of women and children through interactive methods. We seek to change negative notions, attitudes and misinformation towards gender-based violence, sexual assault and victimisation.

With our well-thought-out strategies, GIRDLE hopes to build a strong voice and create zero tolerance for such inhuman crimes and anti-social practices.

For observation and comment, please contact GIRDLE by sending an SMS to: 081 2212 5147, 0812 430 2985, 0708 535 4482.

What this book is about

Aduke Coker has never followed the dictates of society. She has weathered the many storms that were thrown into her childless marriage, but one raging storm besieges her, and she has to flow with the tide or be overrun by it.

CUT OFF is a story based on actual events. It tells of the ordeal of Aduke, haunted by barrenness and pressured by her husband and his mother, as the last resort for pregnancy, to go for 'female circumcision' (FGM) in adulthood.

Did she resist or accept the savage cut? The book tells it all!

WHAT THEY SAY ABOUT CUT-OFF

"*Cut Off* is a compelling true-life story of a professional woman pitted against the traditional practice of FGM, leading to tragic consequences. A heartrending and harrowing look into one woman's fate, which unfortunately, is the fate of millions of women and girls in this world. A must read." – Leila Walsh, writer and member of the Planned Parenthood Federation of America (PPFA).

"*Cut Off* is riveting, petrifying, elucidatory and engaging. People should support this caused and make sure you gift someone this book, it's totally worth it." – Ekene Odigwe, Presenter, Federal Radio Corporation of Nigeria, Human Rights Ambassador.

"The book is highly informative and captures the true reality of silent victims of FGM who are helpless and can't fight back. It's my wish that this book will get to communities where this inhumane act is still deeply rooted; we need to sensitize them with the vital information enclosed in "Cut Off"." – Esther Ijewere, Social Entrepreneur, Columnist (Guardian), activist, author.

"*Cut Off* is a contemporary work that paints the dark, scary but realistic picture of the conflicting values between our past and present. It's a literary battle-cry for help and justice. I hope everyone does not just read it but joins in the fight to end FGM everywhere." – Ms Samuel Abosede Olufunmilayo, co-founder, Girly Girly Ideas, Nigeria.

"Wow! Indeed a "cut off" – this is breathtaking! *Cut Off* brings to fore the stark reality of the horrendous practice called FGM in Nigeria. With words crafted beautifully, the author brings home the challenges of domestic violence/FGM the average Nigerian woman is faced with as epitomised by the character of Aduke. – Mrs Oluwayomi Osuntokun, Female Activist/Advocate (Women Empowerment).

"The use of imagery in the first chapter "In the belly of a forest" is so rich and almost transports the reader to the scene. I could actually feel what Aduke was feeling because of the language and the rich imagery, and that was what I enjoyed most about the book... the story is quite touching and heartbreaking." – Mrs Nike Fakorede, Educationist (Imaginations School).

"*Cut Off* is a very interesting read. It is intriguing, intense and suspense-filled. The plot creates a vivid image in the reader's mind in such a way that one feels he/she is alive in the story. The way the writer maintains a thread from the bus ride while adding a twist of flashbacks and still links up the story almost at the end still in the bus is indeed very captivating. The plot in its entirety is so captivating that I was held spellbound." – Abraka Patricia, Human Rights Activist, Girl-Child/Child's Rights Advocate.

"The concept behind this book amazes me. As an anti-FGM campaigner, the book brought out all the various misconceptions people have about FGM. *Cut Off* also shows its versatility by featuring other forms of gender-based violence (wife battery, rape etc). *Cut Off* is not only campaigning against FGM but also against other forms of GBV." – Somto Ugwu, Barrister and Human Rights Advocate (SIRP).

"I read through the book with admiration for the great piece it is. Quite educative and spoke to a number of issues too. It is a great book that captures your attention and keeps you engrossed till the end." – Mrs. Olamide Falana, Ondo State DPP Governorship Candidate 2016, Human Rights Activist, Adolescent Reproductive Health Expert.

"*Cut Off* is a call for action on the part of all, men especially, to help in putting an end to the travails of voiceless young girls and women in our society. It is educative and interesting as it touches on other aspects of domestic violence, which has claimed the lives of many. The 'cut' has to be put to an end because its disadvantages surpass its supposed advantages." – Chidi Ikpeme,

Human Rights Activist (CYP).

"*Cut Off* is mercurially gripping and will have you sitting on the edge of your seat, empathising with womanhood and their 'fate' in the society. This book will break you down and make you reflect, 'Which woman is going through this right now?' We must stop this cruel practice of FGM. *Cut Off* is a must-read for all!" – Mrs Dupe Oteri, Author "My Menstrual Cycle and I".

9 781861 513199